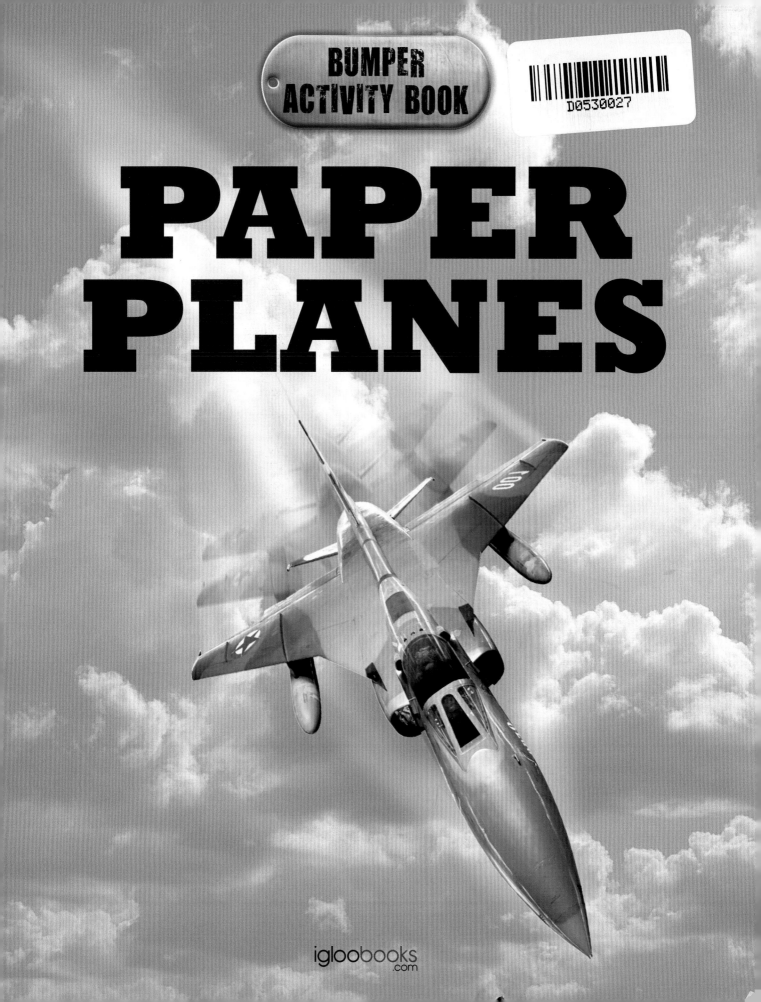

BUMPER
ACTIVITY BOOK

D0530027

PAPER PLANES

Intrepid Pioneers

People have always dreamed of being able to fly. There are winged creatures in Greek and Roman mythology, the ancient Chinese tried to take off using kites and, in the late 1400s, Leonardo da Vinci designed a number of flying machines. The study of birds led to the invention of ornithopters, but flights in these flapping wing machines usually ended in disaster, as they crashed to the ground, killing or injuring the pilot. Hot air balloons and airships were more successful, as was Otto Lilienthal's hang glider in the 1890s, but these craft were really floating rather than flying.

The race to lift a heavier-than-air machine off the ground was won by the Wright Brothers with Flyer 1 in 1903. The Wrights wanted to keep their invention to themselves. However the French were inspired by their success and, over the next few years, France led the way in building planes that broke records for speed, altitude, and distance. It is thanks to these pioneers that French words such as fuselage and aileron are now part of the language of aviation.

Birdmen

Anyone who has seen the Star Wars film, Revenge of the Sith, or played a Dune computer game will be familiar with ornithopters – flying machines with flapping wings. Modern planes have rigid fixed wings, but the inventors of the earliest heavier-than-air flying machines were inspired by watching birds, so their craft were based on wings that moved up and down. Artist Leonardo da Vinci was among the first to design such a machine – he was drawing ornithopters over 500 years ago.

As far as we know, da Vinci's ornithopter never took to the air, but in the years that followed many men lost their lives trying to fly using wings made of feathers, leather, or cloth. Generally they took off from a cliff or tall building and crashed to the ground seconds later. The first successful ornithopter flight is said to have taken place in Germany in 1781, but the first confirmed and witnessed flights were in the 1870s when Alphonse Pénaud and Gustave Trouvé both flew model ornithopters in Paris. Pénaud's model was powered by rubber bands and Trouvé's by gunpowder.

While others were concentrating on the development of the ornithopter, British scientist, Sir George Caley was designing a piloted glider. He, too, experimented with model planes, before building a glider large enough to carry a man. First, he tried it out using animals as passengers, then, in 1853, he persuaded his coachman to test the machine. The young man landed safely after flying for 130 m (140 yards). This was the first recorded manned, heavier-than-air flight and Caley is considered to be the world's first aeronautical engineer.

Ornithopters can only fly if they are launched into the air from a height and even then they are gliding rather than flying. Humans are simply too heavy, and not strong enough to fly by using their arms and legs to flap the wings.

1853 first manned
flight in Caley's glider

TIME LINE

| 1840 | 1850 | 1860 | 1870 | 1880 |

Time Line

1490 Leonardo da Vinci designs ornithopters and other flying machines. (Page 3)

1870 Alphonse Pénaud and Gustave Trouvé fly model ornithopters in Paris. (Page 3)

1913 Armand Deperdussin's revolutionary racing plane wins the Gordon Bennett Cup in Chicago. (Page 8)

1781 The first successful ornithopter flight is claimed to have taken place in Germany. (Page 3)

1903 The Wright Brothers make the first powered heavier-than-air flight in Flyer 1. (Page 6)

1958 Boeing's first jetliner, the 707, makes its inaugural flight from New York to Paris with 111 passengers. (Page 24)

1947 Sound barrier broken by U.S. Air Force pilot Chuck Yeager in the Bell X-1 (Page 28)

1941 The Lancaster bomber makes its maiden flight. (Page 12)

1962 U.S. rocket research plane X-15 penetrates outer space. (Page 28)

1952 The Comet, the world's first passenger jet, makes its first commercial flight. (Page 22)

1943 Maiden flight of the Constellation (Page 21)

1964 The Lockheed SR-71 (the Blackbird) makes its first test flight. (Page 14)

1971 The first DC-10s are delivered. (Page 26)

1969 The world's first widebody jet, the Boeing 747, makes its inaugural flight. (Page 26)

1969 Concorde makes its first test flight. (Page 28)

1983 The MiG-29 Fulcrum, Russia's most important tactical fighter, enters service. (Page 16)

1917 The Fokker Dr-1, one of the best dogfighters of World War I, goes into production. (Page 11)

1933 Boeing introduces the 10-passenger 247, the first modern commercial airliner. (Page 52)

1927 Charles Lindbergh completes the first solo transatlantic flight in Spirit of St. Louis.

1935 First flight of the DC-3, said to be the most successful passenger plane ever flown. (Page 19)

1940 The Vought Corsair is the first fighter to fly at 400 mph (644 km/h)

1939 The first jet aircraft, the Heinkel HE 178, takes off. (Page 22)

1937 Frank Whittle and Hans von Ohain simultaneously design the jet engine. (Page 22)

1941 The Lancaster bomber makes its maiden flight. (Page 12)

1939 Pan Am's Boeing 314 flying boat flies from New York to Southampton.

1938 The Spitfire, Britain's most successful World War II fighter plane, goes into production.

1988 The Airbus A380, the first fly-by-wire airliner, enters service.

2005 The superjumbo A380 completes its first flight. (Page 30)

1989 The B-2 Spirit bomber makes its first flight. (Page 18)

1994 Boeing's widebody fly-by-wire 777 makes its first test flight.

FUTURE: First Virgin Galactic passenger flights to space due to take off. (Page 32)

The Wright brothers

American brothers Wilbur and Orville Wright worked tirelessly in the workroom behind their bicycle shop, pursuing their dream of making a controlled, powered, heavier-than-air flight. They were self-taught engineers who used scientific methods to test their designs – flying kites and gliders, and experimenting with model wings in their own wind tunnel, before putting their ideas into practice.

At the end of 1903, the Wright brothers were ready to test their first proper plane, named Flyer 1. It had a wooden framework, which was covered with fabric, and was powered by a small motor that drove twin propellers behind the wings. One of their most important breakthroughs was the ability to control and steer the aircraft using an elevator at the front of the plane and a rudder at the back. There were no seats – the pilot just lay on his stomach on the lower wing and steered by moving a cradle attached to his hips, which adjusted the rudder. Wilbur and Orville tossed a coin to see who would pilot the plane.

Wilbur won but stalled, so Orville took a turn. His flight lasted 12 seconds and he flew 36.5 m (120 ft). The brothers made two more flights and Wilbur managed to stay airborne for 59 seconds, covering 260 m (853 ft). Wilbur and Orville went back to their bicycle shop and, over the next two years, they built the Flyer II, followed

TIME LINE

1840	1850	1860	1870	1880

FLYER 1 FACT FILE

Wingspan: 12.29 m (40 ft 4 in)

Length: 6.43 m (21 ft 1 in)

Max. take-off weight: 338 kg (745 lbs)

Maximum speed: 30 mph (48 km/h)

Crew: 1

Engines: one straight-4 water-cooled 12 horsepower piston engine

Flyer 1 is generally considered to be the first successful plane. This type of aircraft is called a canard (French for duck) biplane, because what would normally be the tailplane is stretched out in front of the pilot, like a duck's neck.

by Flyer III. In 1905, Wilbur set a record in Flyer III when he flew over 34 miles (55 km) in 38 minutes, landing only when he ran out of fuel. Wilbur died of typhoid in 1912, but Orville devoted his life to aviation until his death in 1948.

1903 Flyer 1 takes off

0   1900   1910   1920   1930   1940

Revolutionary racer

The Reims air race was so popular, it was followed by a series of races across Europe and the United States, and the demand for racing planes led to great advances in aircraft design. In 1913, a revolutionary, streamlined monoplane racer, built in France by Armand Deperdussin's company, SPAD, won a number of trophies and achieved the record-breaking speed of 126.67 mph (203.85 km/h).

Deperdussin was a cabaret singer and silk merchant before he founded his aviation company. At the time, planes were normally built around a wooden or metal framework, which was covered with fabric, but Deperdussin's designer developed the "monocoque" (single shell) fuselage, made of plywood. The plane's thin wings were covered with linen and strengthened by bracing wires attached to supports in front of the cockpit. The result was a very light, but strong, racing plane.

The plane's first major victory was in the Gordon Bennett Cup race held in Chicago in 1912. The following year, in Reims, the Deperdussin won again, achieving an average of 124.6 mph (200.5 km/h) and beating the world speed record three times, with a maximum speed of 126.7 mph (203.85 km/h).

SPAD's success came to a sudden end in 1914 when Deperdussin was arrested for fraud and forgery. He was jailed for five years and Louis Blériot rescued the company, which went on to supply fighter planes to the French, British, American, Italian, Belgian, and Russian squadrons during the First World War.

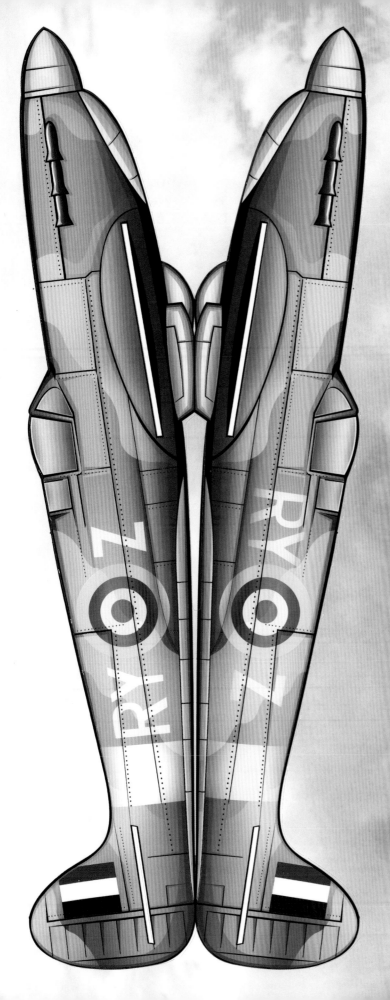

Spitfire

1 Carefully press out all the sections of the plane. Fold the unprinted sides of each section together and stick with double sided tape.

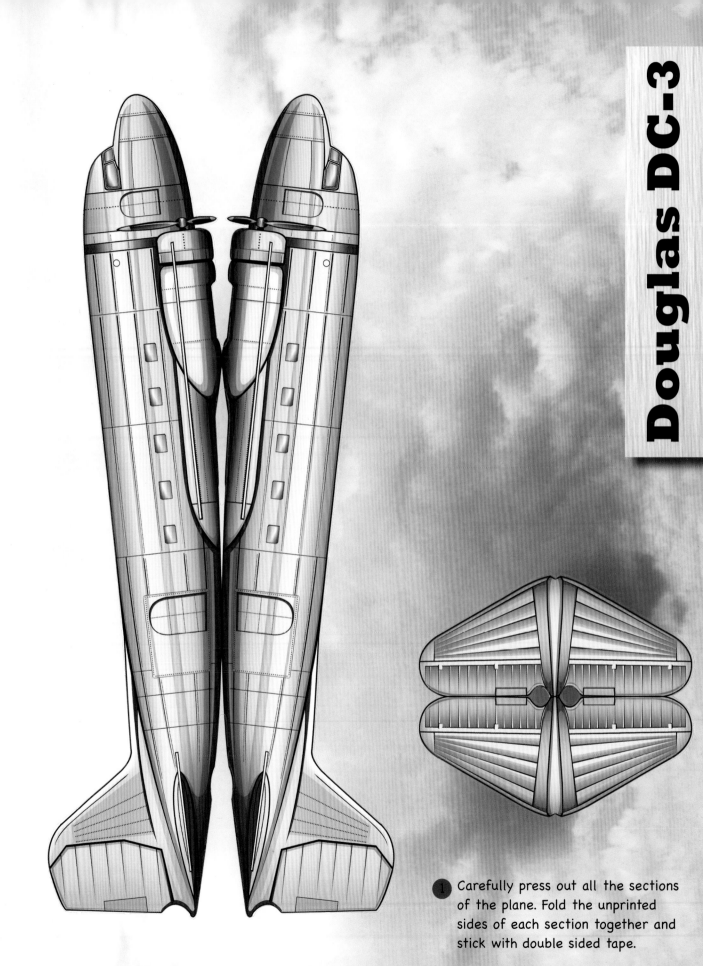

Douglas DC-3

1 Carefully press out all the sections of the plane. Fold the unprinted sides of each section together and stick with double sided tape.

Douglas DC-3

2 Slide the wings and the tailplane into the slots in the fuselage.

3 Now try flying your plane. You might need to add a weight to the nose – experiment with various items such as paper clips, or try taping a small coin to the front of the plane.

Spitfire

2 Slide the wings and the tailplane into the slots in the fuselage.

3 Now try flying your plane. You might need to add a weight to the nose – experiment with various items such as paper clips, or try taping a small coin to the front.

DEPERDUSSIN MONOCOQUE RACER FACT FILE

Wingspan: 6.65 m (21 ft 10 in)

Length: 6.1 m (20 ft)

Weight: 612 kg (1,350 lbs)

Maximum speed: 126.7 mph (203.85 km/h)

Engines: one 160 horsepower Gnôme
14-cylinder twin row air-cooled rotary engine

*With its streamlined design, the
Deperdussin Monocoque was the
world's fastest pre-war plane.*

1912 Deperdussin Monocoque
wins the Gordon Bennett Cup

0   1900   1910   1920   1930   1940

Aerial Attackers

Less than 100 years ago, troops, and equipment were transported overseas by ships, and battles took place on land or at sea. Following the invention of airships and planes in the early 1900s, warfare changed forever. Now it was possible to spy on the enemy from the sky and drop bombs on distant targets. Soon planes were equipped with machine guns and the first fighters took to the air.

Although aircraft played an important role in the First World War, during World War II the development of planes suddenly accelerated as the first long range bombers and jet fighters went into action. The struggle to dominate the air reached its peak with the Battle of Britain in 1940, when allied airmen fought the German Luftwaffe in the skies, above southern England.

The Cold War brought the fear of nuclear attack and reconnaissance planes were designed to spy on hostile countries. Equipped with photographic, infrared and radar sensors, these aircraft often incorporated the latest "stealth" technology, and include some of the fastest planes in the military.

Today, the air force is at the forefront of any battle and is usually the first to engage the enemy.

The first war planes

At the start of World War I, planes were used as scouts to check out the enemy's position, rather than as fighting machines. Soon, Dutch engineer Anthony Fokker perfected a machine gun that could fire through a plane's propeller without hitting the blades and the fight for control of the air began.

The Fokker Dr-1 offered excellent visibility and a fantastic climb rate, thanks to its three wings.

Equipped with two machine guns, the Fokker Dr-I triplane was the first true fighter. Although it wasn't the fastest plane in the sky, it was light and agile and could outmaneuver most opponents in a dogfight. It is one of the most well-known planes of the First World War, because it was flown by Germany's most famous ace, Baron Manfred von Richthofen, who brought down around 80 enemy aircraft. Von Richthofen was known as the Red Baron because he painted his plane bright red. He was shot and killed while flying over France in his Fokker a few months before the end of the war.

1916 Handley Page bomber takes to the air

1917 Fokker Dr-1 goes into production

TIME LINE

1910   1920   1930   1940   1950

Lancaster bomber

There were great advances in aircraft design in the years between the two world wars. The fighter pilots of World War I enjoyed showing off their skills in stunt displays and air races, and the large cash prizes on offer encouraged the development of faster planes. Instead of wood and canvas, most planes were now made of metal and fitted with more powerful engines. During World War II the speed, range and bomb load of bombers increased and, following the invention of the jet engine in the 1930s, the first jet fighters took to the air.

The Lancaster was one of the most successful bombers of the Second World War, flying 156,000 missions and dropping over 600,000 tons of bombs. Powered by four engines, it achieved a speed and lifting ability that no other second world war plane could match. It could almost carry its own weight again. Each plane carried a massive bomb load of 81,656–10,000 kg (18,000–22,000 lbs) and it was the only bomber that could drop the 10,000 kg (22,000 lb) "grand slam" – the heaviest bomb ever used.

TIME LINE

1910   1920   1930   1940   1950

1941 Lancaster bomber makes its first flight

The crew, made up of the pilot, engineer, navigator, radio operator, bomb aimer, mid-upper gunner, and rear gunner, endured long flights in cramped and very cold conditions – the gunners, exposed in their turrets, even suffered from frostbite at times.

LANCASTER BOMBER FACT FILE

Wingspan: 31.09 m (102 ft)

Length: 21.18 m (69 ft 5 in)

Max. take-off weight: 28,636 kg (63,000 lbs)

Maximum speed: 280 mph at 15,000 ft (448 km/h at 5,600 m)

Range: 2,700 miles (4,320 km) with minimal bomb load

Crew: 7

Engines: four 280 horsepower Rolls-Royce Merlin XX piston engines

Weapons: eight Browning machine guns in three turrets.
Up to 10,000 kg (22,000 lbs) of bombs, typical load 6,350 kg (14,000 lbs)

Three Lancaster bombers come under attack by German Messerschmitts. The average Lancaster survived for just three weeks in combat over Europe, before it was shot down. Between 1942 and 1945 over 3,000 were lost in action.

The Blackbird

At the end of the 1950s, the American CIA were looking for a super-fast spy plane that could fly anywhere in the world and have photographs back on an officer's desk the same day.

The solution was the supersonic Lockheed SR-71 – known as the Blackbird because it was painted blueish-black – which entered service in 1966. With a cruising speed above Mach 3 (over three times the speed of sound), the Blackbird was three times faster than a jumbo jet and flew twice as high. The plane's absolute speed record of just over 2,193 mph (3,529 km/h) and altitude record of nearly 25,929 m (85,069 ft) were unbeaten during its years of service.

When the Blackbird cruised at Mach 3, it became incredibly hot and stretched by several inches, so all its parts had to be loosely fitted to allow for expansion. For this reason, the fuel system was not properly sealed when the plane was on the ground and fuel would leak out onto the runway. There was little danger of fire, however, as the plane ran on JP-7 fuel which is difficult to ignite. The aircraft would take off with a light fuel load and fly for seven minutes so the parts could expand, before its six large tanks were refueled in mid-air ready for its mission.

There were over 1,000 attempts to shoot the Blackbird down, but it was so fast it could accelerate away from a surface-to-air missile. However, it was difficult to land – it came in so fast that it needed a tail chute to slow it down and 11 of the 32 that were built crashed on landing.

TIME LINE

1910   1920   1930   1940   1950

The Blackbird didn't have a tail – instead two fins on top of the enormous engines helped to steer the plane. It was one of the first aircraft to be specially shaped to avoid being spotted by radar. It cost $140 million a year to keep the Blackbird fleet flying and their job was eventually taken over by spy satellites, so they were retired in the 1990s.

SR-71 BLACKBIRD FACT FILE

Wingspan: 16.94 m (55 ft 7 in)

Length: 32.73 m (107 ft 5 in)

Max. take-off weight: 52,250 kg (140,000 lbs)

Maximum speed: Mach 3.3

Maximum altitude: over 25,929 m (85,000 ft)

Range: over 2,000 miles (3,200 km)

Crew: 2

Engines: two Pratt and Whitney J-58 axial-flow turbojets with afterburners, each producing 32,500 pounds of thrust

The Blackbird's skin was made of titanium alloy to withstand the 600-degree heat caused by air friction at Mach 3. It was painted with a blueish-black paint containing tiny iron balls. This released heat two and a half times faster than unpainted titanium and also helped the plane to avoid radar detection.

1964 Lockheed SR-71 makes its first test flight

0   1970   1980   1990   2000   2010

MiG-29 Fulcrum

The MiG-29 (given the codename Fulcrum by NATO) was one of the Soviet Union's most important fighter planes during the final years of the Cold War and it is still in use today. Its development dates back to 1969, when the Soviet government learned of U.S. plans to build the F-15 Eagle. Realizing that the U.S. plane would be superior to any in their fleet, the Russians immediately commissioned a new lightweight fighter-interceptor that became operational in 1983.

Spectators at the Farnborough Air Show in 1988 were astounded by the MiG-29's agility as it performed aerobatics beyond the normal capabilities of a fighter plane. Its light body and powerful engines mean it can fly straight up like a rocket, even with a full load of missiles, while its ability to make tight, fast turns give it an advantage over most other planes in a dogfight.

The MiG-29 is a silent hunter thanks to its infrared search and track system, which allows it to scan the sky for heat given out by other aircraft, while avoiding giving out radar or radio signals itself.

This plane doesn't need a runway – it can take off or land on a rough dirt track or in a field.

The jet intakes can be closed off to stop mud, stones, or snow being sucked into the engines.

MIG-29 FULCRUM FACT FILE

Wingspan: 11.4 m (37 ft 3 in)

Length: 17.4 m (57 ft)

Maximum speed: 1,510 mph (2,430 km/h)

Range: 932 miles (1,500 km)

Crew: 1

Max. take-off weight: 18,500 kg (40,785 lbs)

Engines: two 8,300-kg (18,298-lb) afterburning thrust RD-33K turbofans

Fixed weapons: one GSh-30L cannon with 150 rounds

The MiG-29 is a deadly dogfighter thanks to its agility and the HMCS (Helmet Mounted Cueing System), a target sight mounted on the pilot's helmet, so that weapons are aimed directly where he is looking.

1983 The MiG-29 enters service

60   1970   1980   1990   2000   2010

Stealth bomber

How do you hide a plane that is 52.5 m (172 ft) wide? This was the problem facing the designers of the B-2 Spirit bomber when they were asked to develop a replacement for the outdated B-52. The U.S. government wanted a plane that could carry bombs halfway across the world in just a few hours and it had to be invisible to the enemy.

It took almost 10 years and billions of dollars to complete the top secret project. Each B-2 cost over $1 billion, which is just under double its weight in gold! The design is unlike any other plane – it looks like a giant boomerang. The aircraft is flat in profile and its black finish means it cannot be seen against the night sky. The engines are buried deep within the plane to reduce their noise, and the exhaust gases are cooled so their heat can't be picked up by infra-red scanners or heat-seeking missiles. Most cleverly of all, the plane is almost undetectable by radar – it appears on the screen about the same size as a sparrow, thanks to its shape, which works like a curved mirror, and the use of radar-absorbent materials. The B-2 travels just below the speed of sound and has a range of 6,900 miles without refueling. Its first mission was during the war in Yugoslavia in 1999. It has since been used in Afganistan and Iraq.

The B-2's flying wing design means that the whole aircraft generates lift, making it very efficient.

TIME LINE

1989 B-2 Spirit makes its first flight

1960   1970   1980   1990   2000

Passenger Planes

During the early years of passenger flight, air travel wasn't a very pleasant experience. Because aircraft cabins weren't pressurized, planes had to fly at lower altitudes, where they were affected by turbulence, so passengers suffered from air sickness, as well as deafening engine noise and cold air. Airlines realized that they would have to make air travel more comfortable if they wanted to attract more passengers.

The Douglas DC-3 made air travel available to many more people. From the mid 1930s, it carried passengers across continents in comfort and gradually planes began to replace trains as the most popular way to travel long distances.

The first jet planes were developed during the Second World War. When the war was over, jet bombers were converted into passenger planes and soon the first jetliners were commissioned. Boeing 707s started flying across the Atlantic in the late 1950s, replacing the Pan Am flying boat service. As more people could afford to fly, larger planes were needed, leading to the development of the jumbo jet, and now the superjumbo A380.

In future, a trip to the moon could be as common as hopping across the Atlantic – tickets are already on sale for the first passenger flights into space!

Air travel takes off

At the beginning of the 1930s most airlines made their money carrying mail and filled any extra space on their planes with passengers. When the United States' government cut the payments for mail deliveries, American airlines looked for planes that could carry more people. In 1933, Boeing brought out the 10-seater 247 and Douglas followed with the 14-seater DC-2. A larger version, the DC-3, had 21 seats and could travel across America, stopping just once to refuel.

At first it looked as if the future of air travel between the continents lay with sea planes, or flying boats. Planes were not able to fly long distances without refueling and, at the time, there were few airfields where they could land. However, flying boats could touch down on rivers or lakes, or in the sea close to small islands where they could refuel and restock.

In the mid 1930s Pan American Airways launched its Clipper fleet, flying to South America and across the Atlantic and the Pacific oceans. These were spacious and luxurious flying boats, where freshly prepared meals were served on linen-covered tables. The Yankee Clipper carried 74 passengers with sleeping quarters for 36 – it even had a honeymoon suite and dressing rooms.

Sea planes have two floats in place of wheels and the fuselage of the plane stays above the water. The fuselage of a flying boat floats in the water like the hull of a ship.

TIME LINE

1934 Clipper flying boat service launched

1943 Constellation makes its first flight

1910   1920   1930   1940   1950

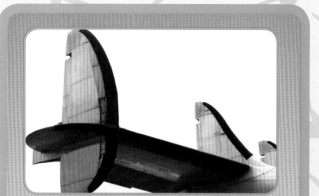

The Constellation is easily recognized by its unusual triple tail with three vertical fins. The plane needed a large tail surface for better control, but a large single fin would not have fitted into most aircraft hangars at the time.

LOCKHEED CONSTELLATION (L-1049G) FACT FILE

Wingspan: 38.47 m (126 ft 2 in)

Length: 35.42 m (116 ft 2 in)

Cruising speed: 354 mph (570 km/h)

Cruising height: 7,620 m (25,000 ft)

Range: 5,400 miles (8,700 km)

Passengers: 62-95

Engines: four Wright R-3350-DA3 Turbo Compound 18-cylinder turbosupercharged radial engines

The landing gear of the Constellation needed to be tall so the large propellers could clear the ground.

During World War II more airfields were built and the speed and range of planes increased, so they could cross the oceans without stopping on the way. Flying boats were replaced by planes such as the Lockheed Constellation, which could travel 3,000 miles and cruise at 280 mph. It was the fastest passenger plane in the sky, with a top speed of 340 mph, thanks to its four powerful engines with their 4.6-m (15-foot) propellers.

The Constellation was the first pressurized airliner, which meant it could fly at 20,000 feet. As this was above most turbulence, passengers could enjoy a more comfortable flight. With its dolphin-shaped body and unusual tail, the Constellation is still considered one of the most beautiful planes in the world.

60   1970   1980   1990   2000   2010

Entering the jet age

British engineer Frank Whittle and German scientist Hans von Ohain were both developing the first jet engine at the same time, but they didn't know about each other's work. Von Ohain was introduced to aircraft designer Ernst Heinkel and between them, in 1939, they created the He-178, the world's first jet plane. Whittle's Gloster E28/39 took to the air two years later. At first Whittle was angry because he thought von Ohain had stolen his idea, but when he found out that this wasn't the case, the two men became friends.

A jet engine works by sucking air in at the front and pulling it through a series of spinning compressors, which squeeze as much air as possible into a combustion chamber. The air in the chamber is mixed with fuel and set alight. This produces hot gases that shoot backward through the exhaust nozzle pushing the plane forward.

The world's first jet aircraft, the single-seat Heinkel He-178, took to the air just a week before the start of World War II, reaching a speed of over 400 mph (644 km/h). The German air force didn't take any interest in the small barrel-shaped monoplane, which might have changed the course of the war if it had been developed further. The He-178 was taken to the technical museum in Berlin, where it was destroyed in an air raid in 1943.

At the start of the jet age, jet engines were only used in military planes. However, commercial air travel was changed forever when British engineers incorporated the jet engine into a passenger plane, the de Havilland Comet, in 1949. The Comet started flying passengers in 1952, but after three crashes during 1953 and 1954, the plane was grounded. The cause was found to be cracks spreading from the edges of the plane's square windows which led to the depressurization and destruction of the aircraft. Windows with rounded corners were installed in all Comets, but it took four years for the planes to start flying again.

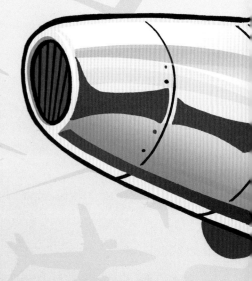

The world's first jet aircraft, the Heinkel He-178, made aviation history when it flew at over 400 mph (644 km/h) in August 1939.

TIME LINE

1939 Heinkel HE-178 takes off

1910   1920   1930   1940   1950

HEINKEL HE-178 FACT FILE

Wingspan: 7.2 m (23 ft 3 in)

Length: 7.48 m (24 ft 6 in)

Weight (empty): 1,620 kg (3,572 lbs)

Maximum speed: 435 mph (700 km/h)

Range: 125 miles (200 km)

Crew: 1

Engine: single HeS.3B turbojet

60   1970   1980   1990   2000   2010

The first big jetliners

The Boeing 707 was one of the earliest jet airliners and it was much smoother and faster than the propeller planes it replaced. In 1958, Pan American Airways launched a transatlantic 707 service between New York and Paris and soon 707s were flying all over the world. Its only real rival, the Douglas DC-8, entered service a year later, but thanks to its headstart and the fact that the Comet had been grounded, Boeing led the market for the rest of the 20th century.

Because of its limited engine power, the Boeing 707 needed very long runways to take off and had problems getting airborne in hot or high places, where the air is less dense. The VC10, which started flying in 1962, was designed to operate in such conditions and, for a while, it looked set to take over from the 707. However, as airports lengthened their runways, the VC10 lost its advantage.

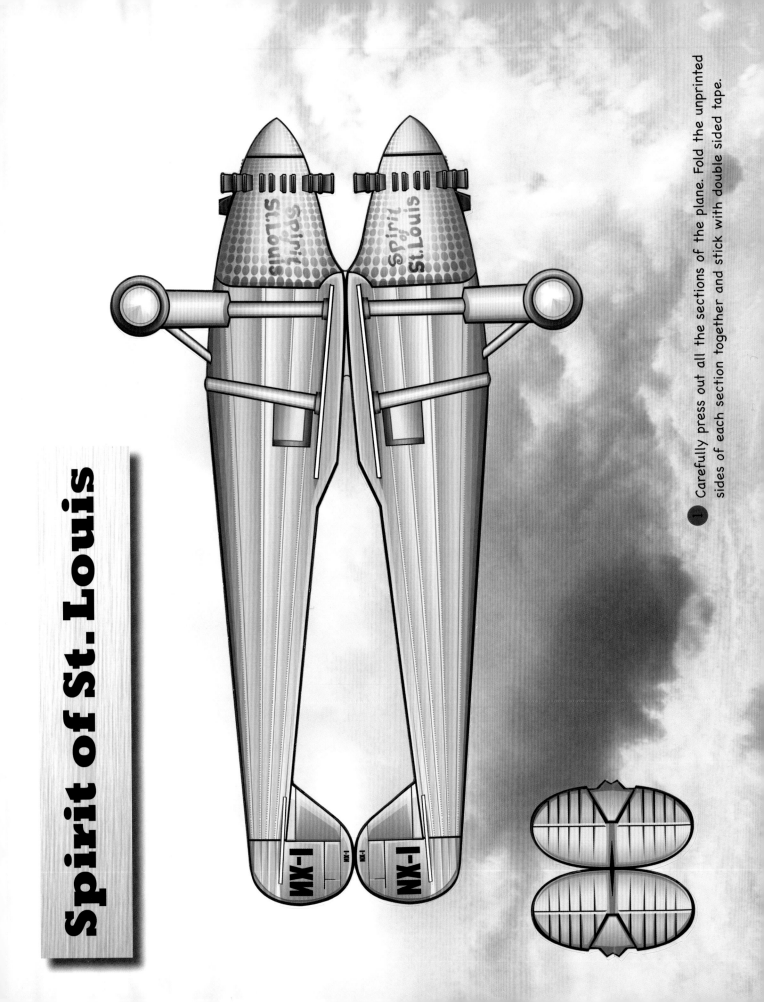

Spirit of St.Louis

1. Carefully press out all the sections of the plane. Fold the unprinted sides of each section together and stick with double sided tape.

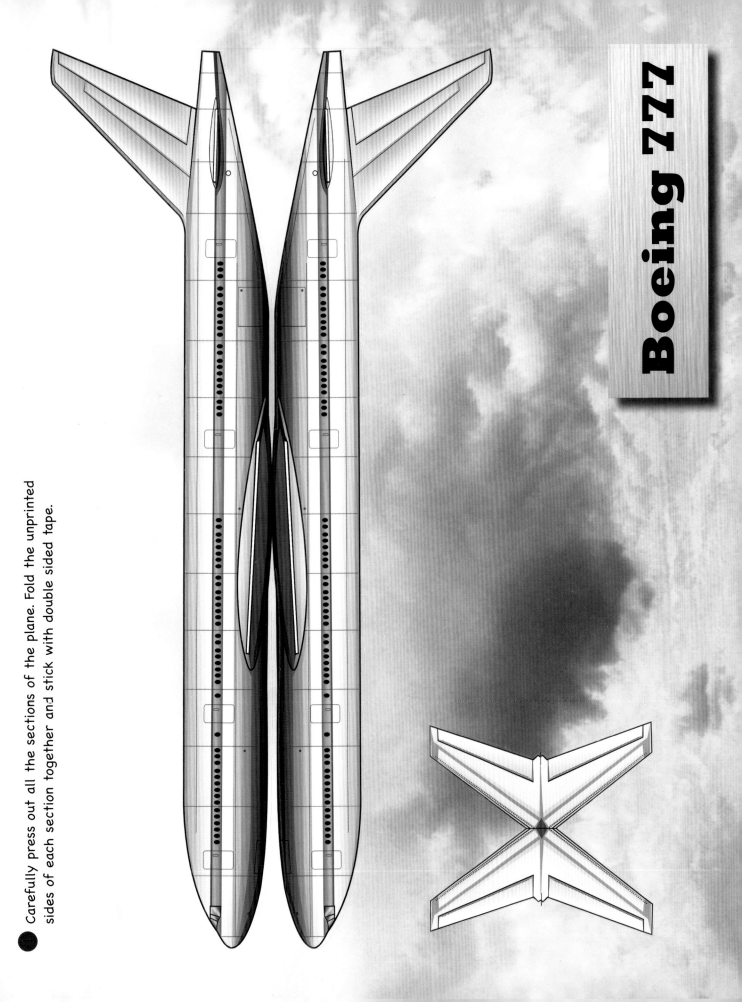

● Carefully press out all the sections of the plane. Fold the unprinted sides of each section together and stick with double sided tape.

Boeing 777

Boeing 777

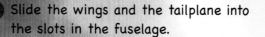

2 Slide the wings and the tailplane into the slots in the fuselage.

3 Now try flying your plane. You might need to add a weight to the nose – experiment with various items such as paper clips, or try taping a small coin to the front of the plane.

Spirit of St. Louis

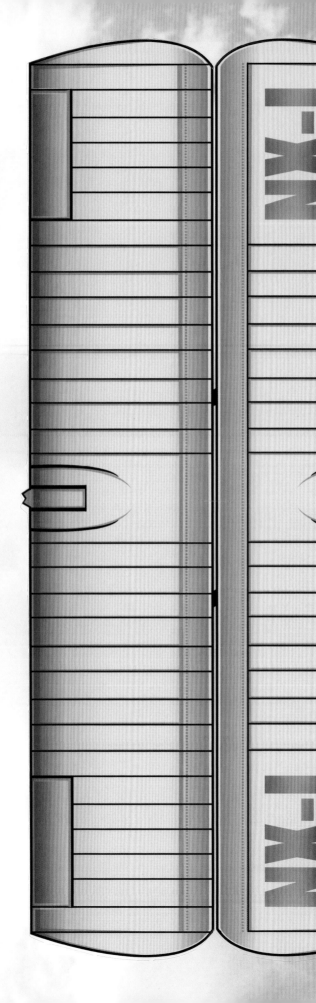

2 Slide the wings and the tailplane into the slots in the fuselage.

3 Now try flying your plane. You might need to add a weight to the nose – experiment with various items such as paper clips, or try taping a small coin to the front of the plane.

John F. Kennedy was the first U.S. president to enter the jet age when a modified 707 was added to the "Air Force One" fleet. He commissioned the plane's blue and white design, which is still used today.

BOEING 707-320B FACT FILE

Wingspan: 44.42 m (145 ft 9 in)

Length: 46.6 m (152 ft 11 in)

Max. take-off weight: 151,320 kg (333,600 lbs)

Maximum speed: 627 mph (1,009 km/h)

Cruising speed: 550 mph (885 km/h)

Cruising height: 10,500 m (34,448 ft)

Range: 5,757 miles (9,265 km)

Passengers: 147-202

Engines: four Pratt & Whitney JT3D-3 turbofans or four Pratt & Whitney JT3D-7 turbofans

The Boeing 707 was the first truly successful commercial airliner. Over 1,000,000 were built between the late 1950s and 1978.

1970　　　1980　　　1990　　　2000　　　2010

Jumbo jets

By the 1970s more people could afford to travel by air and planes had replaced ocean liners as the usual way to cross the Atlantic. Pan American Airways were looking for a giant plane to transport larger numbers of passengers between the United States and Europe and, in January 1970, the first Pan Am Boeing 747 left New York for London. The 747 was the first of the jumbo jets – wide-bodied planes with two aisles between rows of eight to ten seats, carrying up to 600 passengers. It was soon followed by the McDonnell Douglas DC-10.

The DC-10 was originally designed as a two-engine plane, but a third engine was added to the tail so that it had enough power to take off from runways that were too short for the heavier 747. Although the engines were twice as powerful as those of earlier airliners, the DC-10 was quieter, and passengers enjoyed the spacious cabin with its wider seats and aisles. The plane was also popular with pilots, but during the 1970s the DC-10 suffered a number of crashes and became known as a dangerous aircraft. Changes were made to the design of the plane and it is now considered to be one of the safest airliners of its age.

DC-10-30 FACT FILE

Wingspan: 50.41 m (165 ft 4 in)

Length: 55.5 m (182 ft 1 in)

Max. take-off weight: 259,459 kg (580,000 lbs)

Fuel capacity: 138,720 l (36,650 gallons)

Cruising speed: 600 mph (965 km/h)

Cruising height: 9,449 m (31,000 ft)

Range: up to 6,220 miles (10,010 km)

Passengers: 250-380

Engines: three General Electric CF6-50A turbofans

The four-engine Boeing 747 is easily recognized by the hump created by the upper deck, which is usually used by first class passengers. The wings are swept back to reduce the wingspan, so that the plane fits into existing hangars.

1970 First Boeing 747 leaves New York for London

1971 First DC-10s delivered

1970   1980   1990   2000   2010

Mach 2 and beyond

The first person to fly faster than the speed of sound (mach 1), was an American test pilot called Chuck Yeager. In 1947 he reached mach 1.06 (700 mph, 1,126.5 km/h) in the bullet-shaped Bell X-1, which was launched from a Boeing B-29. In 1962, another U.S. plane, the X-15, achieved a top speed of mach 6.7 (4,520 mph, 7,274 km/h) – four times faster than a speeding bullet!

Concorde's first commercial flights began in 1976. With a cruising speed of mach 2, the supersonic airliner cut the flying time between London and New York in half, to just three and a quarter hours. It was popular with business people and celebrities, but the plane only had space for 100 passengers, and had to carry one metric ton of fuel for each person, so ticket prices were sky-high. In 2000 a ticket cost over $8,000!

Flying at the edge of space

At Concorde's cruising height of over 11 miles (17.7 km) high, the sky is a deep purple-blue and the view of the land below is like looking at a map. Passengers could even see the curvature of the earth through the plane's tiny windows.

When planes break through the sound barrier they produce a sonic boom – a sound similar to thunder, caused by the shockwaves when an aircraft reaches supersonic speed. The noise meant that Concorde was not allowed to fly at top speed over land, so its routes were restricted to long sea crossings.

Apart from the prototypes, only 16 Concordes were ever produced. The planes were too expensive for most airlines and the last five were sold for just one French franc each!

When Concorde flew at mach 2 it heated up and expanded, so it grew 30 cm (1 ft) longer during a flight.

Because of its delta wings, Concorde had to take off at steep angle and its long pointed nose would have blocked the pilot's view. Engineers solved the problem by giving Concorde a drooping nose that could be raised and lowered during the different stages of a flight.

CONCORDE FACT FILE

Wingspan: 25.46 m (84 ft)

Length: 61.66 m (202 ft)

Max. take-off weight: 181,436 kg (408,000 lbs)

Fuel capacity: 119,280 l (25,250 gallons)

Take off speed: 250 mph (402 km/h)

Cruising speed: mach 2 (1,320 mph, 2,124 km/h)

Cruising height: 18,290 m (60,000 ft)

Range: 4,500 miles (7,242 km)

Passengers: 100

Engines: Four 38,050-lb-thrust Rolls Royce/SNECMA Olympus 593 Mk 610 turbojets with afterburners

Concorde had a streamlined, needle-shaped body, which was just 2.7 m (9.5 ft) wide – much smaller than a jumbo jet which is over 6 m (20 ft) wide. This meant that the passengers did not have much space inside the cabin. The sharp pointed nose and narrow fuselage, combined with the delta (triangular) wings, allowed the plane to penetrate the air and cruise at supersonic speed. However, the wing design meant Concorde had to take off and land at higher speeds than normal aircraft.

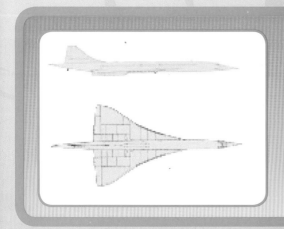

1969 Concorde's first test flight

1962 X-15

1970   1980   1990   2000   2010

The superjumbo A380

The length of two blue whales, with a wingspan as wide as a soccer field, the double-decker Airbus 380 is the biggest passenger plane ever built. It's not the largest aircraft to take to the skies, though. This title goes to the An-225 Mriya Cossack, built in 1988 to carry the Soviet space shuttle. The second largest was the Hughes HK-1 (the Spruce Goose), a massive wooden flying boat built in America during the Second World War to transport tanks and troops. It only made a short trial flight because the war was over by the time it was ready for service.

The A380 can carry about 555 passengers in economy, business and first class cabins, but it could take up to 840 if the plane were filled with economy seats. There are even plans for a stretched version, which could carry up to 1,000! Some airlines are thinking of installing duty-free shops, lounges, gyms, hot-tubs, libraries, and even a casino in the large cabin space. Airports are being redesigned to accommodate this giant of the skies, as most terminals don't have the space to park a plane of this size, and if two were to arrive at the same time, passengers could spend longer finding their luggage and clearing customs than they did on the plane!

A Giant Jigsaw Puzzle

Parts for the A380 are made all over the world. Roads have been widened and special barges and canals have been built to transport the massive sections. The front and rear parts of the fuselage are made in Germany and transported by ship to Mostyn docks in north Wales. Meanwhile the enormous wings, made in nearby Broughton, are delivered to the docks by barge and loaded onto the ship. These parts are then shipped to Brittany, in western France, and swapped for larger, assembled sections, which are delivered to Bordeaux. Then the ship goes on to Spain to collect the belly and tail of the plane and take them back to Bordeaux. The doors are made in India and other parts come from the United States. The sections are put together like a giant jigsaw puzzle in Toulouse, in south-west France. Finally the fully assembled airliners are flown to Hamburg in north Germany for painting and furnishing.

The double-decker design of the A380 means the aircraft is lighter than a wider-bodied single deck jet carrying the same number of passengers. The 8 in the plane's name represents the cross-section view of the twin decks.

TIME LINE

| 1910 | 1920 | 1930 | 1940 | 1950 |

A380 FACT FILE

Wingspan: 79.8 m (261 ft 10 in)

Length: 73 m (239 ft 6 in)

Max. take-off weight: 560,196 kg (1,235,000 lbs)

Fuel capacity: 310,000 l (68,343 gallons)

Take off speed: 186 mph (299 km/h)

Cruising speed: 560 mph (902 km/h)

Cruising height: 13,100 m (43,000 ft)

Range: 9,383 miles (15,100 km)

Passengers: 555 typical, 840 maximum

Engines: Four 302kN (67,890 lb) thrust class Rolls-Royce Trent 900 or Engine Alliance (General Electric-Pratt & Whitney) GP-7200 turbofans

The A380, compared here to an American football field, is the third largest plane ever built. The largest is the Russian An-225, which is now used to carry ultra-heavy freight (some weighing as much as 50 elephants) or super-sized cargoes, which are transported piggy-back style on the plane's roof.

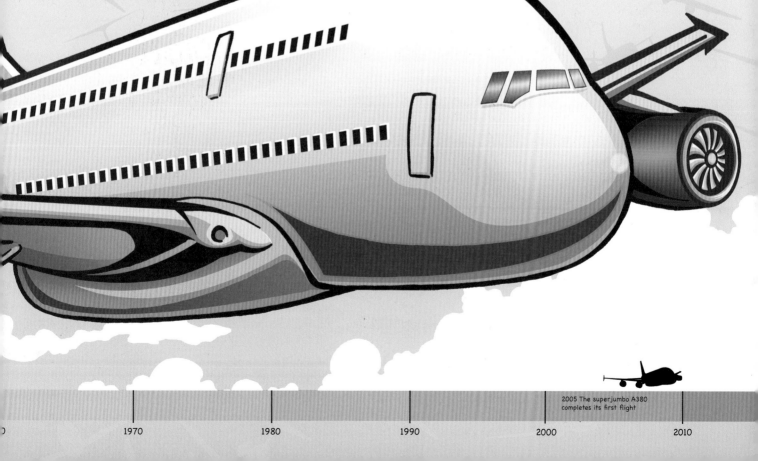

The final frontier?

One day boarding a spaceplane could be as common as hopping onto a jumbo jet. Until now the only planes to reach space have been the X–15, SpaceShipOne and SpaceShipTwo. SpaceShipTwo (SS2), has been developed in partnership with Virgin Galactic to carry passengers into space in the future.

Virgin Galactic plans to fly passengers to a maximum height of over 80 miles, where they will experience six minutes of weightlessness. Tickets cost approx. $200,000 and include three days of medical preparation and space flight training. Future space tourists are already making reservations for the first flights.

SpaceShipTwo won't lift off from a launch pad like a rocket. Instead, like the X–15 and SS1, SS2 will be lifted to around 10 miles above sea level by a carrier aircraft – in this case, a twin-engine turbojet named Eve, aka White Knight Two – before being released. As the spaceship accelerates to a speed faster than a bullet, those on board will see the sky turn

from blue to purple, then to indigo and black. The stars will be visible even though it is daytime and the view from the large porthole windows will be over 1,000 miles in any direction. The powerful rocket motor is fueled by a combination of nitrous oxide (laughing gas) and rubber which produces almost no pollution.

Return to Earth

The spaceliner will have adjustable wings so that, at the end of the flight, it can transform from a sleek spaceship to a glider that floats gently back through the atmosphere without overheating.

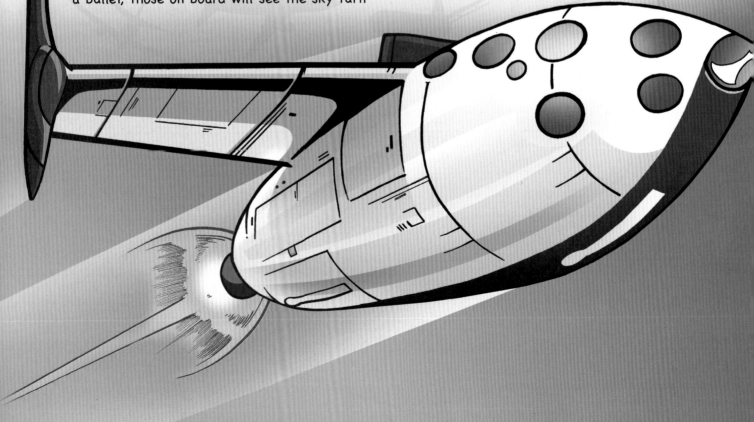